S0-BIP-541

y of Congress Control Number: 2011925167

BN 978-0-545-20886-4 (hardcover)
BN 978-0-545-20887-1 (paperback)

18 19

rinted in Malaysia   108
edition, September 2011
ed by Cassandra Pelham
y Kazu Kibuishi and Phil Falco
Director: David Saylor

Publishe

The
re

Libra

IS

2019

Fir
Edi
Book design
Creativ

AMULET

KAZU KIBUISHI

BOOK FOUR
THE LAST COUNCIL

AN IMPRINT OF

SCHOLASTIC

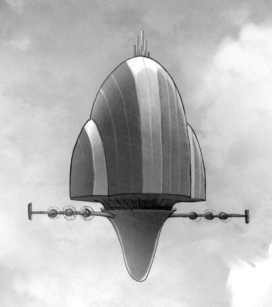

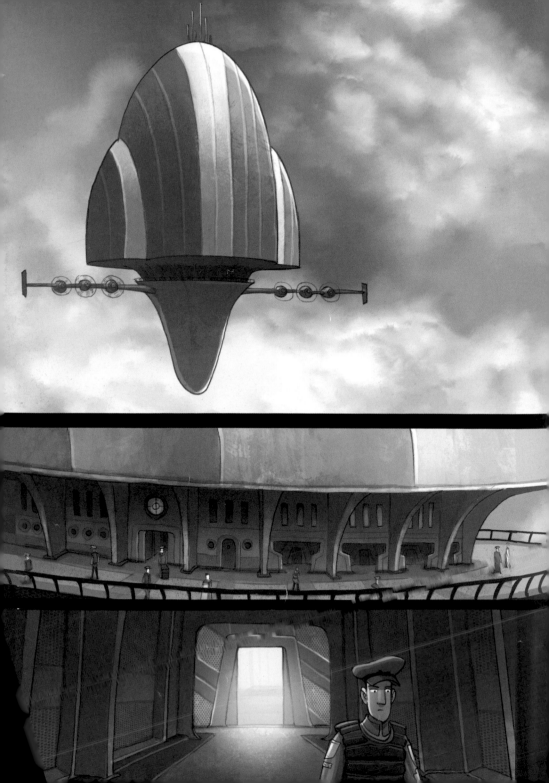

NOT YET. YOU WILL BE SOON.
WHEN YOU BEGIN TO REALIZE THE TRUE WEIGHT OF YOUR ACTIONS...
...YOU WILL AWAKEN TO BECOME THE PERSON THIS WORLD NEEDS YOU TO BE.

EMILY, EVERYONE'S READY TO GO NOW.

WHO'S THERE?

IT'S JUST ME, MAX.

YOU TOOK A NAP, AND I THINK YOU WERE HAVING A NIGHTMARE.

I HAVE A HEADACHE.

MAYBE SEEING CIELIS WILL HELP MAKE IT GO AWAY.

COME ON.

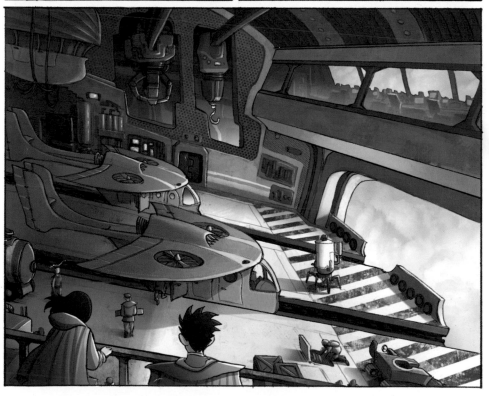

WATCH YOUR STEP.

I DON'T TRUST THESE GUYS, MOM.

I STILL DON'T SEE WHY THEY HAD TO TAKE TRELLIS AND LUGER PRISONER.

I'M SURE THEY HAVE THEIR REASONS.

THEY KNOW MORE THAN WE DO, NAVIN.

YOUR MOM'S RIGHT, KID.

YOU DON'T KNOW SQUAT.

BUT TRELLIS AND LUGER ARE OUR FRIENDS!

IF THERE'S ONE THING I'VE LEARNED IN MY LIFE, IT'S THAT YOU CAN NEVER TRUST AN ELF.

ESPECIALLY IF THAT ELF IS THE ELF KING'S SON!

THE OTHERS ARE READY FOR TRANSPORT, SIR.

THANK YOU, LEN.

TELL DUNCAN WE'RE READY AS WELL.

YES, SIR.

THESE MEN, THEY TREAT YOU LIKE YOU'RE THEIR LEADER.

WHY?

MY FATHER WAS CAPTAIN OF THE CIELIS GUARD.

I TOOK HIS PLACE WHEN HE PASSED AWAY.

SO I'M THE CAPTAIN UNTIL THE COUNCIL DECIDES ON A REPLACEMENT.

I HAVE TO ADMIT THAT POLICE WORK NEVER REALLY SUITED ME.

MY REAL AMBITION IS TO BE ON THE COUNCIL.

IT SHOULD BE YOUR GOAL, TOO.

WHY?

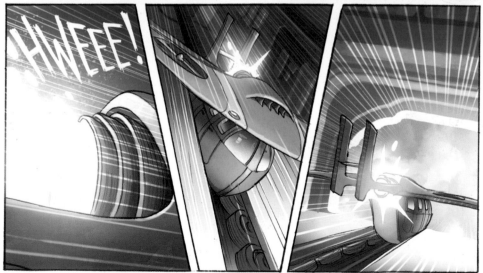

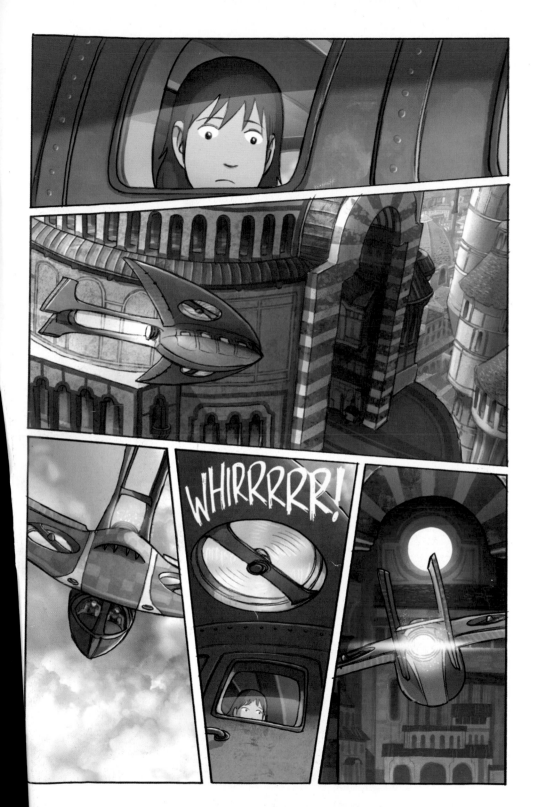

WHIRRRRR!

YOU ARE NOT AUTHORIZED TO GO BEYOND THIS POINT.

BUT I'M WITH THEM.

ONLY STONE-KEEPERS AND THEIR FAMILIES ARE ALLOWED ACCESS TO THE ACADEMY.

BUT I WAS ORDERED BY THE GUARDIAN COUNCIL TO DELIVER THE STONEKEEPER MYSELF.

DO YOU HAVE PAPERWORK?

HEY, LEON --

PAPERWORK?

LET ME SPEAK TO YOUR SUPERIOR!

JUST LET IT GO.

I NOTICE WE'RE NO LONGER FOLLOWING THE OTHERS.

WHERE ARE YOU TAKING US?

ASKING THE WRONG QUESTIONS CAN GET YOU IN TROUBLE AROUND HERE.

I SUGGEST YOU JUST STAY QUIET AND DO AS YOU'RE TOLD.

YOU CAN SAVE YOURSELF AND THE OLD MAN FROM A LOT OF PAIN.

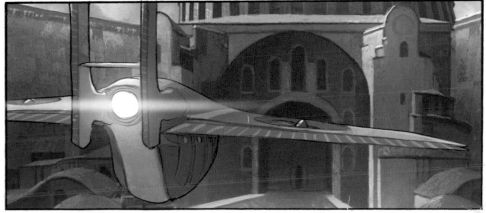

WELCOME TO YARBORO PRISON.

A LITTLE BIRD TOLD ME THAT YOU ARE THE SON OF THE DEVIL HIMSELF.

WHEN I HEARD THAT THE ELF KING WAS YOUR FATHER, I ASKED TO BE IN CHARGE OF YOU, PERSONALLY.

NOW, YOU SHOULD KNOW THAT MY FAMILY WAS KILLED BY YOUR PEOPLE BACK IN THE WAR.

AND I'M THE KIND OF MAN WHO DOESN'T FORGET THINGS TOO EASILY.

AS YOU CAN SEE, WE HAVE THE FINEST JAILHOUSE FACILITIES IN THE SKIES.

THIS IS CELL BLOCK FOUR, AN AREA RESERVED FOR OUR FOREIGN GUESTS.

THE COUNCIL PLANS TO PUT YOU TWO ON TRIAL FOR WAR CRIMES.

YOU'LL BE STAYING IN HERE UNTIL YOU ARE SUMMONED.

I DON'T WANT ANY TROUBLE, UNDERSTAND?

IF I FIND ANY EXCUSE TO COME IN HERE AND REGULATE,

TRUST ME, I'LL TAKE IT.

IF I CAN JUST GET THIS COLLAR OFF,

I CAN USE MY STONE TO BREAK US OUT.

IT IS WHERE THE MOST POWERFUL STONEKEEPERS IN HISTORY HELD COURT.

THIS IS THE GRAND HALL OF THE ACADEMY.

AND NOW WE'LL HAVE THE OPPORTUNITY TO JOIN THEIR RANKS.

MAX,

IS THIS THE GUARDIAN COUNCIL'S CHAMBER?

YES.

HOW DO I GET INSIDE?

WE NEED TO SPEAK WITH THEM.

I'M SORRY, EMILY.

THAT'S NOT HOW THINGS WORK AROUND HERE.

YOU CAN'T SIMPLY GO AND BOTHER THEM UNANNOUNCED.

WE DON'T HAVE TIME FOR THIS, MAX!

WE NEED TO TELL THEM ABOUT THE ELF KING BEFORE IT'S TOO LATE!

AND YOU DON'T THINK THEY ALREADY KNOW?

THE GUARDIAN COUNCIL KNOWS EVERYTHING.

YOU WILL HAVE YOUR AUDIENCE WITH THEM.

BUT YOU MUST BE PATIENT.

NOW FOLLOW ME.

I'LL SHOW YOU TO YOUR NEW LIVING QUARTERS.

THIS MUST BE A MISTAKE.

THIS PLACE IS JUST SO... SO FANCY.

I ASSURE YOU THIS IS NO MISTAKE.

YOUR DAUGHTER IS ALREADY HELD IN VERY HIGH ESTEEM HERE IN CIELIS.

I DON'T LIKE THIS PLACE, EM.

WHERE ELSE CAN WE GO, NAVIN?

THESE PEOPLE ARE SUPPOSED TO BE THE ONLY ONES WHO CAN HELP US.

I ALWAYS THOUGHT WE WERE ON OUR OWN.

YOU MAY NOT BELIEVE ME, BUT I CAN UNDERSTAND YOUR HESITATION.

I WANT TO ASSURE YOU THAT EVERYTHING WE HAVE DONE HAS BEEN FOR YOUR BENEFIT.

YOUR FRIENDS WERE TAKEN ASIDE TO ALLOW YOU TO FOCUS.

THEY ARE QUITE SAFE, AND ARE BEING TREATED AS GUESTS.

TOMORROW WILL BE YOUR FIRST DAY IN THE ACADEMY.

THE COUNCIL IS VERY EXCITED TO SEE HOW YOU PERFORM IN THE TESTS.

WE CAME HERE TO ASK THE COUNCIL FOR HELP.

I DIDN'T COME HERE TO JOIN THEM, MAX.

YOU NEED TO BEGIN TAKING THIS OPPORTUNITY A LITTLE MORE SERIOUSLY, EMILY.

THESE TESTS DETERMINE WHO AMONG US ARE THE STRONGEST STONEKEEPERS.

AND ONLY THE STRONGEST WILL EARN THE RIGHT TO LEAD OUR ARMY AGAINST THE ELF KING.

IT IS YOUR DUTY TO HELP US HOWEVER YOU CAN.

NOW, MAKE SURE YOU GET PLENTY OF REST TONIGHT.

YOU'RE GOING TO NEED IT.

NO.

EVER SINCE WE ENTERED THE ACADEMY GROUNDS, THE STONE'S POWER HAS FELT SO WEAK.

SOMETHING HERE IS AFFECTING IT.

AT LEAST WE'RE BEING TREATED NICELY.

BUT, MOM, I'M GETTING A BAD TINGLY FEELING ABOUT THIS PLACE. WE SHOULD GO.

NAVIN'S RIGHT, MOM.

YOU SHOULD AT LEAST TRY TO APPLY YOURSELF HERE AND NOT BE SO QUICK TO JUDGE.

DEFEATING THE ELF KING IS THE ONLY WAY WE'RE GOING TO MAKE OUR WAY HOME, RIGHT?

WELL, THESE PEOPLE SEEM LIKE THEY COULD BE VERY POWERFUL ALLIES.

YOU CAN DEFINITELY USE THEIR HELP.

BUT CAN'T YOU SEE THERE'S SOMETHING WRONG WITH THIS PLACE, MOM?

DON'T LOOK AT ME LIKE THAT.

I'M NOT BLIND, EMILY.

AS YOU GROW UP, YOU'RE GOING TO LEARN THAT ALMOST EVERYWHERE YOU GO, YOU'RE GOING TO FIND "SOMETHING WRONG" WITH THE PLACE.

THAT'S JUST THE WAY LIFE IS.

YOU JUST HAVE TO BE WILLING TO FOLLOW THEIR SYSTEM AND DO WHAT YOU CAN TO MAKE THINGS RIGHT.

AS LONG AS YOU'RE DOING WHAT'S RIGHT, THINGS SHOULD WORK THEMSELVES OUT.

AND YOU MIGHT EVEN HELP THE PEOPLE AROUND YOU ALONG THE WAY.

CONSIDERING OUR SITUATION, I DON'T THINK I HAVE MUCH OF A CHOICE, MOM.

COME HERE.

WE'LL BE ALL RIGHT.

WE'LL BE FINE AS LONG AS WE STAY TOGETHER.

WELL, THIS IS PRETTY DISAPPOINTING.

THE PLACE IS LIKE A GHOST TOWN.

WAS IT ALWAYS LIKE THIS, CHIEF?

NO.

IT IS STRANGELY QUIET NOW.

THIS USED TO BE ONE OF THE BUSIEST STREETS.

LET'S FIND SOMETHING TO EAT. I'M FAMISHED.

THIS PLACE LOOKS OPEN.

42

WHERE ARE YOU GOING, CHIEF?

SOMETHING STRANGE IS GOING ON HERE.

MAYBE THIS GIRL CAN PROVIDE US WITH ANSWERS.

AND MAYBE SOME FOOD?

HMM.

THIS WAY!

CHARLIE'S CAFE

IN HERE!

HEY, WAIT.

I NEED TO TALK WITH YOU.

HELLO?

HELLO?

ANOTHER EMPTY HOLE-IN-THE-WALL.

LOOKS LIKE BUSINESS IS SLOW IN THIS CITY.

CREAK!

SEE, MOM?

I BROUGHT YOU SOME CUSTOMERS.

HELLO, MA'AM.

HELLO.

JUST TAKE A SEAT ANY-WHERE.

MY MOM MAKES THE BEST YUKMO PIES!

CAN I TALK TO YOU IN PRIVATE?

MOM, IT'S OKAY.

YOU NEED TO LEAVE HERE FOR YOUR OWN SAFETY.

THIS TOWN IS CURSED.

IF YOU STAY, THEY WILL LOCK YOU UP AND KILL YOU LIKE THE OTHERS.

WHO WILL LOCK US UP?

THE ELF KING?

NO.

THE GUARDIAN COUNCIL.

THE COUNCIL?

THEY WERE THE ONES WHO SENT ME ON THIS MISSION.

HOW MANY YEARS AGO?

THE COUNCIL IS NO LONGER WHAT IT ONCE WAS.

CLICK

THE DOOR IS LOCKED.

BUT, DAD, THE COUNCIL ISN'T REAL.

THEY'RE GHOSTS, JUST LIKE THE ONES THAT HAUNT THE CITY!

WHAT ARE THESE GHOSTS YOU'RE TALKING ABOUT, KID?

A FEW YEARS AGO, I SAW A GROUP OF PEOPLE I RECOGNIZED, BUT THEY ACTED LIKE STRANGERS.

THEY TOOK OVER THE CITY IN A MATTER OF DAYS.

AND WHAT MAKES YOU BELIEVE THEY'RE GHOSTS?

LIKE I SAID, I RECOGNIZED THEM.

BUT THESE PEOPLE --

-- THEY'RE SUPPOSED TO BE DEAD.

THAT'S ENOUGH!

REMEMBER WHAT WE TALKED ABOUT?

BUT, DAD --

I CAN'T JUST BOTTLE UP THE TRUTH.

MY PARENTS ARE AFRAID BECAUSE THEY KNOW WE'RE ALWAYS BEING WATCHED!

BUT I DON'T CARE!

ALYSON!

YOU'RE NOT GHOSTS.

AND YOU'RE NOT FROM HERE.

SO YOU MUST BE HERE TO HELP US, RIGHT?

I --

LISTEN, KID.

THE TRUTH IS, WE CAME HERE LOOKING FOR HELP.

NOT THE OTHER WAY AROUND.

SORRY TO DISAPPOINT YOU.

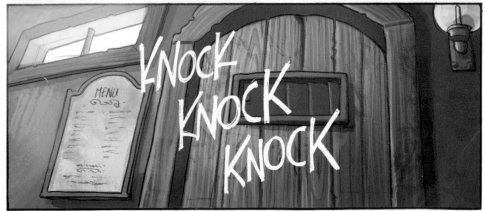

KNOCK KNOCK KNOCK

IT'S THE GUARD.

IS THERE SOMEPLACE WE CAN HIDE?

NO.

DAD!

WE HAVE TO HELP THEM!

THERE'S NO USE HIDING HERE.

THE GUARD WILL FIND THEM QUICKLY.

THEY CAN ESCAPE THROUGH THE KITCHEN.

THE GUARD IS GOING TO TRY AND TAKE US, TOO.

SO I WANT YOU TO GO WITH YOUR FRIENDS.

WHAT ABOUT YOU AND MOM?

WE'LL BE FINE.

WE CAN STAY HERE AND DISTRACT THEM.

PLEASE TAKE CARE OF ALY.

SHE IS EVERYTHING TO US.

ALY'S INSTINCTS HAVE RARELY BEEN WRONG.

SO I HOPE SHE'S RIGHT AND YOU MANAGE TO HELP US ALL.

I'LL SEE WHAT I CAN DO.

LET'S GO!

THIS WAY!

HURRY!

YOU OKAY?

I'M FINE.

WE'LL BE SAFER TAKING THE BACKSTREETS.

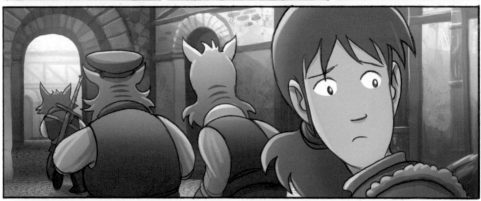

KNOCK KNOCK! KNOCK!

SHK!

COLE?

LISTEN TO ME, KID.

YOU'RE GOING TO HAVE TO FLY.

IF YOU DON'T, THESE PEOPLE ARE GOING TO EAT YOU, UNDERSTAND?

YOU HAVE NO IDEA WHAT I'M SAYING, DO YOU?

HERE THEY COME, COGSLEY!

WHAT ARE YOU DOING?!

THIS IS FOR HIS OWN GOOD!

YOU'LL THANK ME FOR THIS, SOMEDAY.

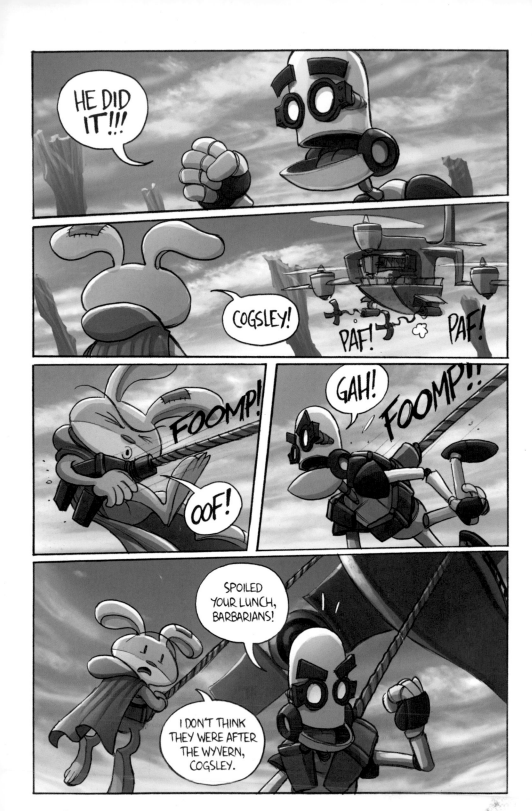

WHIRRRR

K-CHUNG!

UNGH!

HM.

VERY INTERESTING.

YOU'RE AN OLDER MODEL.

HEY, YOU'RE NOT EXACTLY A SPRING CHICKEN, EITHER!

WELL, YOU BOYS LOOK HARMLESS ENOUGH.

JUST MAKE YOURSELVES COMFORTABLE AND HOLD ON TO SOMETHING.

WHERE ARE WE GOING?

HOME.

HEY, LOOK, COGSLEY.

YOUR NEW BUDDY DECIDED TO FOLLOW US.

WHAT ARE YOU DOING, KID?!

GO BACK!!

CHIK! CHIK!

WELCOME BACK HOME, SIR!

CECIL, WE HAVE A COUPLE OF NEW RECRUITS.

LOAD UP THEIR MEMORY WITH A CLEANING PROGRAM.

YES, SIR!

HEY! NOBODY'S LOADING ANYTHING INTO OUR BRAINS!

POOMP!

I SAID SIT DOWN.

YOU'RE A STONEKEEPER!

HMPH.

YOU MENTIONED SILAS.

HOW DID YOU KNOW HIM?

WE SERVED TOGETHER ON THE GUARDIAN COUNCIL.

HE LEFT ME THIS.

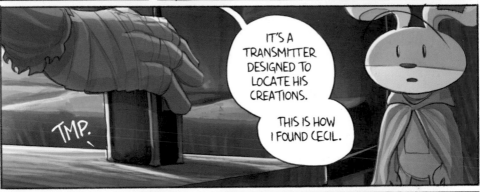

TMP.

IT'S A TRANSMITTER DESIGNED TO LOCATE HIS CREATIONS.

THIS IS HOW I FOUND CECIL.

THE DEVICE SAT QUIETLY FOR YEARS BEFORE IT BEGAN TRANSMITTING ANOTHER SIGNAL.

AND THAT'S HOW I FOUND YOU.

I NEVER GOT TO ASK SILAS WHY HE GAVE ME THIS TRANSMITTER.

IT WAS LONG AFTER OUR TIME ON THE COUNCIL WHEN I LEARNED WHAT IT WAS FOR.

SILAS SAID HE WAS EXILED FROM CIELIS FOR TELLING THE TRUTH.

INTERESTING.

WHY WERE YOU BOOTED OUT?

I WASN'T BOOTED OUT.

I LEFT.

YOU MUST UNDERSTAND THAT SILAS WAS AN ODD MAN.

HE SPOKE HIS MIND FREELY, AND IT WOULD UPSET THE OTHER COUNCIL MEMBERS.

HE WAS EVENTUALLY VOTED OFF THE COUNCIL.

BUT WHAT WOULD PROMPT THE COUNCIL TO EXILE HIM?

HE WANTED TO DESTROY THE MOTHER STONE.

THE MOTHER STONE?

IT IS WHERE ALL OF THESE COME FROM.

OUR STONE-KEEPER POWERS ORIGINATED FROM A SINGLE SOURCE.

CUT FROM A GEM...

...THAT WAS DISCOVERED BY THE EARLY SETTLERS OF THIS PLANET.

REALIZING THAT THE MOTHER STONE CONTAINED TREMENDOUS ENERGY, THE SETTLERS BURIED IT DEEP BENEATH THEIR FIRST CITY...

...CIELIS, THE ANCIENT CAPITAL OF WINDSOR.

THE ORIGINAL GUARDIAN COUNCIL WAS CREATED TO GOVERN USE OF THE MOTHER STONE. SMALL BITS OF THE POWERFUL GEM WERE CUT AND PRO-VIDED TO THE EARLY SETTLERS OF ALLEDIA TO HELP THEM DEVELOP OUR WORLD.

CENTURIES PASSED, AND HUNDREDS OF STONEKEEPERS WERE BORN. WITH THEIR POWERS THEY BUILT THE FOUNDATION FOR THE GREAT NATIONS OF ALLEDIA, AND ACCELERATED THE DEVELOPMENT OF CITIES ACROSS THE GLOBE.

OF COURSE, MORE THAN A FEW STONEKEEPERS ABUSED THE IMMENSE POWER THAT THE STONES PROVIDED THEM, AND WAGED WAR ON OTHER STONEKEEPERS FOR CONTROL OF THE NATIONS. MANY STONEKEEPERS PER-ISHED IN THESE BATTLES, AND THEIR STONES PERISHED WITH THEM.

BY THE TIME I HAD JOINED THE COUNCIL, ONLY A SMALL SHARD OF THE STONE REMAINED. IT WAS DECIDED THAT CUTTING THE FINAL PIECE WOULD ONLY BE CONSIDERED IF THE COUNCIL NEEDED TO CALL ON ITS POWERS TO HELP DEFEND CIELIS AND THE NATION OF WINDSOR. IT WAS CONSIDERED A LAST RESORT.

YOUR MASTER SILAS FELT THAT IF WE WERE NOT GOING TO USE THE STONE IMMEDIATELY, WE SHOULD DESTROY IT BEFORE IT FELL INTO THE WRONG HANDS.

TO TREAT IT AS AN INSURANCE POLICY, HE REASONED, WAS A DANGEROUS MISTAKE.

HE CRITICIZED THE COUNCIL FOR MAKING DECISIONS BASED ON ITS FEARS, AND HE BELIEVED THAT IF WE CONTINUED DOWN THIS PATH, WE WOULD SEE OUR FEARS REALIZED.

AT THE TIME, I WAS THE YOUNGEST MEMBER OF THE COUNCIL.

AND DUE TO MY INEXPERIENCE, I MADE SOME DECISIONS THAT I WOULD REGRET FOR THE REST OF MY LIFE.

THE FIRST SUCH DECISION WAS TO VOTE IN
FAVOR OF REMOVING SILAS FROM THE COUNCIL.

SHORTLY THEREAFTER, THE ELVES
UNLEASHED A DEVASTATING ATTACK ON
CIELIS AND FORCED THE COUNCIL TO HIDE
THE CITY IN THE CLOUDS.

SSSIP.

AND THEN I BEGAN TO SEE WHAT SILAS SAW.

THE COUNCIL'S EVERY MOVE WAS MOTIVATED BY FEAR AND I WAS JUST TOO YOUNG TO NOTICE IT BEFORE.

I COULD NO LONGER BE A PART OF THEM.

AND YOU JUST... LEFT?

SO I TENDERED MY RESIGNATION.

I BEGAN TO WORK OUTSIDE THE SYSTEM.

I PASSED THE STONE DOWN TO MY SON, AND I TRAINED HIM TO BECOME A BETTER STONEKEEPER THAN I EVER WAS.

HE WAS EAGER TO FIGHT, SO HE SET OUT TO TAKE ON THE ELF KING.

AND WHAT HAPPENED?

THAT'S A STORY FOR ANOTHER TIME.

NOW IF YOU'LL EXCUSE ME...

I HAVE A SUNSET TO CATCH.

YOU'RE WELCOME TO STAY HERE AS LONG AS YOU'D LIKE.

BUT IF YOU WOULD PREFER TO LEAVE, WE CAN PROVIDE YOU WITH A BOAT.

GREAT! WHERE ARE THE PADDLES?

WHAT HAPPENED TO HIS SON?

HE WAS KILLED AND THE STONE RETURNED TO VIGO.

VIGO HASN'T BEEN THE SAME SINCE.

YOU'RE NOT GOING TO GIVE UP, ARE YOU?

WELL, IF YOU WANT TO JOIN OUR CREW, YOU'LL HAVE TO TOUGHEN UP.

YOU CAN START BY WIPING THAT GOOFY GRIN OFF YOUR FACE.

HEY, CHIEF! WHERE ARE YOU GOING?

I NEED TO SPEAK WITH VIGO.

HURRY UP, OR WE LOSE THE SUN!

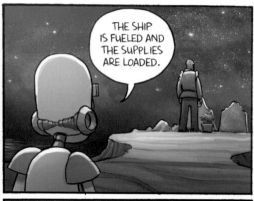

THE SHIP IS FUELED AND THE SUPPLIES ARE LOADED.

WHAT DO YOU THINK, CECIL?

I THINK IT'S HIGH TIME YOU GOT BACK IN THE GAME, SIR.

OF COURSE YOU DO.

THIS IS WHAT I GET FOR LISTENING TO THE TOYS OF A MADMAN.

Miriam Light

Daniel Light

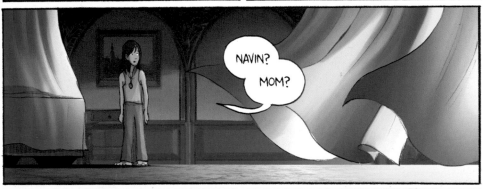

WHO ARE YOU?

HEY!

WHAT HAVE YOU DONE WITH MY FAMILY?!?

YOU HAVE BEEN SUMMONED BY THE COUNCIL.

GOOD LUCK.

SUCH STRANGE STATUES.

MAX?

MY NAME IS RONIN.

AND THIS IS PIERCE.

HEY.

WHAT DID MAX TELL YOU?

THAT YOU'RE THE "CHOSEN ONE" HERE TO SAVE CIELIS?

'CAUSE THAT'S WHAT HE TOLD THE REST OF US.

HE TOLD ME I WOULD BE TESTED.

AND DID HE TELL YOU ABOUT THE CONSEQUENCES FOR FAILING THESE "TESTS"?

YOU DON'T JUST GET TO WALK OUT OF HERE, EMILY.

STONEKEEPERS ARE BROUGHT HERE TO DIE.

STOP SCARING HER, PIERCE.

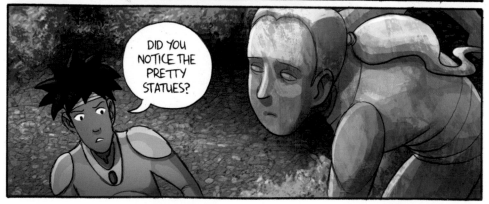

WHEN YOU DIE IN THE VOID, YOU GET TURNED TO STONE.

THE VOID?

BWAAAAAAH

WHAT WAS THAT?

THE COUNCIL.

THE TESTS ARE ABOUT TO BEGIN.

WE NEED TO MEET IN THE CENTER.

FOLLOW US.

YOU COMING?

YEAH, I'LL BE RIGHT BEHIND YOU.

RONIN, WHAT IS THE VOID?

THE VOID IS A SIMULATION.

IT'S A VIRTUAL SPACE WHERE THE COUNCIL SENDS US TO BE TESTED.

THIS WEEK'S TESTS ARE TO BE THE FINAL ONES.

WHOEVER SURVIVES THEM WILL JOIN THE COUNCIL.

AWW, NO.

LOOK WHO'S STILL HERE.

PIERCE!

GLAD TO SEE YOU'RE STILL WITH US!

I FIGURED YOU GUYS WERE TOAST!

FIND ME IN THE VOID AND WE'LL SEE WHO'S THE LAST ONE STANDING.

WE FIGHT EACH OTHER?

WE DO WHATEVER IT TAKES TO SURVIVE.

WHO BROUGHT THE LITTLE TRAITOR?

AND WHY IS HE EVEN STILL ALIVE?

SHOVE!

LOOKS LIKE THE COUNCIL DECIDED TO ABANDON HIM.

YOU HEAR THAT, SHRIMP?

NO ONE WANTS YOU ON THEIR SIDE.

THAT MEANS THE MOMENT YOU STEP INTO THE VOID...

...YOU'RE AS GOOD AS STONE.

I THINK IT'S GONE NOW.

WHAT WAS IT?

A GROUL.

THEY WERE USED BY THE OLD COUNCILS TO GUARD THEIR MOST VALUABLE TREASURES.

I DIDN'T REALIZE THEY STILL EXISTED.

WHAT ARE THEY GUARDING HERE?

THAT'S A GOOD QUESTION.

I DON'T KNOW.

WELL, THE ONE THING I LEARNED ABOUT DIFFICULT CHALLENGES IS THAT YOU DON'T WANT TO FACE THEM ALONE.

WE'RE GOING TO NEED THE OTHERS' HELP WHETHER YOU LIKE IT OR NOT.

AND DON'T FLATTER ME.

IT MAKES ME FEEL WEIRD.

OW.

I CUT MYSELF.

ARE YOU OKAY?

I'M FINE, BUT --

-- YOU'RE NOT SUPPOSED TO BLEED IN THE VOID.

YOU DON'T HAVE TO DO THIS.

WE CAN BOTH LIVE TO FIGHT A LITTLE LONGER.

JUST WALK AWAY.

WHY DELAY THE INEVITABLE, PIERCE?

LET'S FINISH THIS.

RIGHT HERE. RIGHT NOW.

WE NEED TO STOP THEM FROM KILLING EACH OTHER.

IF THEY FINISH EACH OTHER OFF, WE WON'T HAVE TO.

MAX!

I'M NOT GOING TO PLAY THIS GAME!

WE NEED TO FIND A WAY OUT OF THIS!

R-RIGHT.

FASH!

SHWIK!!!

URK!!

LEAVE MY FRIENDS ALONE.

NICE GOING, HAYES!

NOW FOR SOME UNFINISHED BUSINESS.

PIERCE, WAIT.

I CAN HELP YOU.

IT'S A LITTLE LATE FOR THAT, GRIFFIN.

WAIT! YOU HAVE TO LISTEN TO ME!

LISTENING TO YOU IS WHAT GOT US HERE IN THE FIRST PLACE!

BUT I'M ON YOUR SIDE!

I DON'T KNOW WHAT GAME YOU'RE PLAYING, GRIFFIN,

BUT I'D RATHER GET RID OF YOU BEFORE WE ALL FIND OUT.

KRKRKKRKKKK

WHAT WAS THAT?

THE REAL THREAT.

WE SHOULD GET TO HIGH GROUND.

NOW.

DRIP

HUH?

DRIP

DRIP

DRIP

127

EMILY! OVER HERE!

WHERE ARE WE, MAX?

THIS IS THE CISTERN.

IT'S WHERE THE CITY'S WATER SUPPLY COMES FROM.

WHAT ABOUT THE GROULS?

WHY AREN'T THEY FOLLOWING US DOWN HERE?

THEY CAN'T SWIM.

WHAT NOW, GRIFFIN?

I'LL TAKE US TO THE EXIT.

HOW CAN WE BE SURE YOU'RE TELLING THE TRUTH?

LOOK, I'M ONLY TRYING TO HELP.

YOU CAN FOLLOW MY LEAD, OR GO ALONE.

THE CHOICE IS YOURS.

YEARS AGO, I DESIGNED YARBORO PENITENTIARY, BUT IT WAS ONLY AFTER THE BUILDING WAS COMPLETE THAT I REALIZED I HAD MADE A MISTAKE.

I FOUND A SIMPLE DESIGN FLAW THAT WOULD COMPROMISE THE INSTITUTION'S SECURITY.

NOW IMAGINE MY SURPRISE TO SEE THAT THIS FLAW CAN SERVE A GOOD PURPOSE.

EVEN WHEN YOU DON'T KNOW WHAT YOU'RE DOING, YOU KIND OF DO, I GUESS.

THAT'S THE ENTRY POINT. IT'S A GRATE WITH BLIND SPOTS ON ALL SIDES.

NO ONE WILL SEE YOU THERE.

TAP!

THANK YOU, MA'AM. FOR THE LODGING, AS WELL.

THANKS, MRS. PINE, FOR EVERYTHING.

DON'T YOU WORRY ABOUT IT.

ALY, WE DON'T HAVE MANY YOUNG FIGHTERS LEFT IN THIS TOWN, SO PLEASE...

...STAY SAFE.

ALY?

MR. PETERS?

ALY, IT IS YOU!

I -- I DON'T KNOW WHY I WAS PUT IN HERE!

I HAVEN'T DONE ANYTHING WRONG!

DON'T WORRY.

WE'LL GET YOU OUT.

BUT WE NEED TO FIND SOME FRIENDS WHO CAN HELP US.

HAVE YOU SEEN ANY ELVES BEING BROUGHT IN HERE?

I HEARD ABOUT TWO ELVES BEING HELD IN CELL BLOCK FOUR.

BUT, ALY, WHY ARE YOU DEALING WITH ELVES?

LET'S GO.

AND WHO IS THIS HALF-BREED?!

ALY!

YOU MUSTN'T TRUST THEM!

TRUST NO ONE!!

THIS CITY IS AS CORRUPT AS MY HOMELAND.

IF THIS WAS YOUR LAST HOPE, I'D SAY WE'RE ALL IN DEEP TROUBLE.

YOU'RE RIGHT.

THE GUARDIAN COUNCIL HAS BEEN COMPROMISED.

IN ORDER TO SET THINGS RIGHT, I WILL NEED YOUR HELP.

HOLD STILL.

SHING!

NOW GET OUT OF THERE.

YOU TRUST ME OVER YOUR OWN SUPERIORS.

WHY?

YOU FIRST.

146

148

HOW ABOUT THIS TIME YOU FOLLOW MY LEAD?

BE MY GUEST.

FASH!

KRSH!

STAND BACK, SON.

YOU'RE A STONEKEEPER, AREN'T YOU?

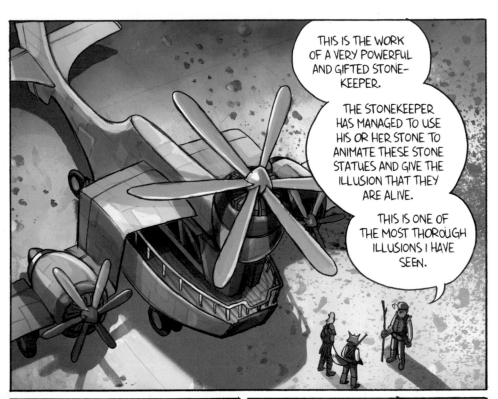

THIS IS THE WORK OF A VERY POWERFUL AND GIFTED STONE-KEEPER.

THE STONEKEEPER HAS MANAGED TO USE HIS OR HER STONE TO ANIMATE THESE STONE STATUES AND GIVE THE ILLUSION THAT THEY ARE ALIVE.

THIS IS ONE OF THE MOST THOROUGH ILLUSIONS I HAVE SEEN.

IF IT WAS SO THOROUGH, THEN WHY DID THE STATUES BREAK APART SO EASILY?

THE ILLUSION'S STRENGTH DEPENDS ON BOTH THE SKILL AND THE PROXIMITY OF THE KEEPER WHO CASTS IT.

IT IS LIKELY THE STONEKEEPER IS FAR AWAY FROM HERE.

SILAS USED TO SAY THAT HIS DISTANCE SPELLS RARELY WORKED WHILE HE WAS UNDERGROUND.

UNDERGROUND.

OF COURSE.

WHERE DID YOU SAY EMILY WENT?

TO THE ACADEMY.

THE ACADEMY...

THE MOTHER STONE, SIR.

WE MUST GET TO EMILY, QUICKLY.

CECIL, GATHER THE OTHERS.

LET'S GO!

WE HAVE NO TIME TO LOSE!

CECIL, WHY DO THE STATUES TAKE THE FORM OF THE DECEASED?

THE POWER TO RE-ANIMATE IS ONE OF THE DARKEST FORMS OF MAGIC THERE IS.

A LARGE AMOUNT OF NEGATIVE ENERGY IS REQUIRED TO KEEP THE ILLUSION ALIVE.

THE IMAGE OF DEATH TRIGGERS THE DARKEST THOUGHTS IN A PERSON'S MIND, AND THE ILLUSION CAN FEED OFF THE FEAR AND SADNESS CREATED.

SIMPLY PUT, THE ILLUSIONS OF THE DEAD ARE STRONGER.

THEN WHOEVER IS CREATING THESE ILLUSIONS MUST NOT CARE VERY MUCH ABOUT OTHER PEOPLE.

UNFORTUNATELY, THAT IS THE MARK OF MANY POWERFUL STONEKEEPERS.

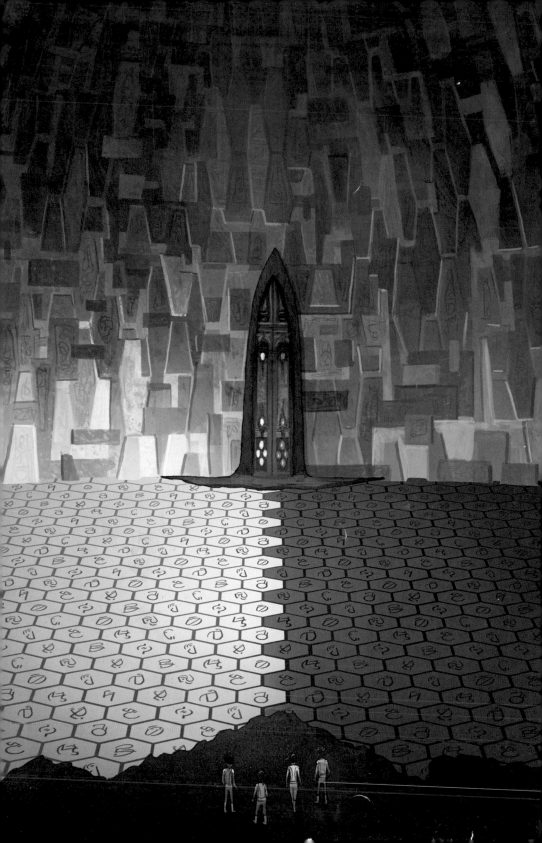

WHAT IS THIS, GRIFFIN?

IT'S AN OLD CIELAN CHILDREN'S GAME.

TWO PLAYERS FOLLOW THE SAME PATH SIMULTANEOUSLY.

ONE PLAYER TAKES THE LIGHT PATH, AND THE OTHER ONE TAKES THE DARK.

IT MUST BE THE KEY TO OPENING THAT DOOR.

WHAT HAPPENS IF YOU STEP ON THE WRONG TILE?

UNGH!

YOU LOSE, APPARENTLY.

AND HOW DO WE KNOW THE PROPER ORDER?

THE MARKINGS ON THE TILES ARE FROM THE OLD CIELAN NUMBER SYSTEM.

THIS DOESN'T LOOK LIKE A PUZZLE AT ALL.

IT IS SIMPLY TELLING US THE CORRECT SEQUENCE OF TILES.

THEN THE CHALLENGE MUST BE TO SEE IF WE CAN WORK TOGETHER.

I FEEL LIKE I JUST SHOWED UP TO A FINAL EXAM I DIDN'T STUDY FOR.

DON'T WORRY, EMILY.

WE'LL BE HERE TO GUIDE YOU THROUGH.

THEY DON'T BELIEVE WE CAN WORK TOGETHER.

THEY THINK WE WOULD RATHER DESTROY EACH OTHER FOR A SPOT ON THE COUNCIL.

I DON'T KNOW ABOUT YOU GUYS, BUT I JUST WANT TO GO HOME.

MAX GOES FIRST.

WHAT?

WANT TO REGAIN OUR TRUST? YOU CAN START RIGHT HERE.

YOU OWE THIS TO US.

165

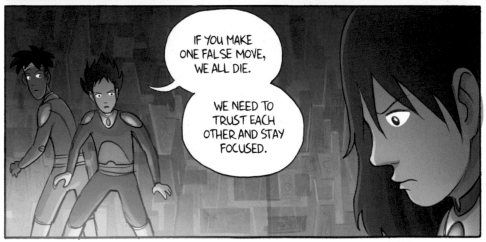

167

MAX, THIS ISN'T THE EXIT.

HOW DO YOU KNOW?

BEFORE I ARRIVED IN CIELIS, MY STONE TOLD ME ABOUT THIS HALLWAY.

IT WARNED ME ABOUT WALKING THROUGH IT.

DID IT TELL YOU WHAT YOU MIGHT FIND AT THE END?

NO.

AND YOU TRUST THE VOICE MORE THAN US?

THERE AREN'T MANY PEOPLE WHO CAN UNDERSTAND WHAT IT'S LIKE TO BE A STONEKEEPER.

THAT'S WHY WE HAVE TO STICK TOGETHER.

COME ON.

WE'RE ALMOST OUT.

FWOOOSH!

THE GUARDS HAVE BEEN ORDERED TO KILL YOUR FAMILY IF YOU TRY AND ATTACK ME.

SO HERE IS YOUR CHOICE.

YOU CAN TRY TO STOP ME WHILE YOUR FAMILY IS EXECUTED --

-- OR YOU LET ME WALK OUT OF HERE --

-- AND I SPARE THEIR LIVES.

HOW DO I KNOW YOU'LL KEEP YOUR WORD?

EMILY!

THANK GOODNESS YOU'RE OKAY!

BEEP!

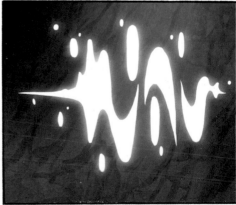

THEY BROUGHT YOU DOWN HERE WITHOUT MAX.

HOW?

THEY USED A THING CALLED A TRANSPORE, JUST BEYOND THE HEXAGON FIELD.

I'LL SHOW YOU.

EMILY --

I SHOULD HAVE LISTENED TO YOU ABOUT THIS PLACE.

I WAS WRONG.

C'MON, MOM --

-- WE NEED TO STAY FOCUSED ON HOW TO SET THINGS RIGHT.

TELL LEN WE'RE IN THE GARDEN.

HAVE THEM MEET US IN FRONT OF THE ACADEMY.

WHO --

YOU'LL HAVE TO DO BETTER THAN THAT, OLD MAN!

SZRAK!

TWIK

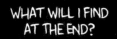

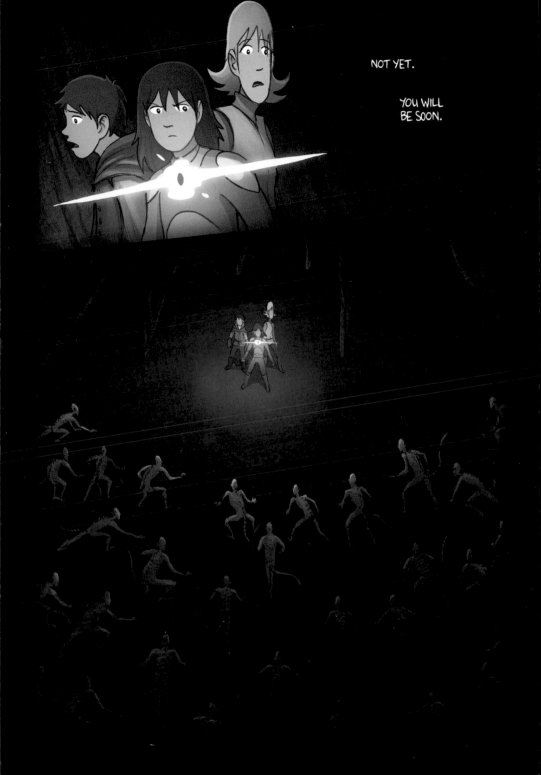

BUT WE'RE THE LAST ONES ON OUR SIDE.

WE ARE THE LAST GUARDIAN COUNCIL.

AREN'T WE?

BACK AT THE ACADEMY, YOU ENCOUNTERED THE LIKENESSES OF SEVERAL YOUNG STONEKEEPERS.

AMONG THEM WERE STUDENTS OF MINE, FROM MANY YEARS AGO.

RONIN WAS MY BEST STUDENT.

SHE WAS THE YOUNGEST STONE-KEEPER TO BE OFFERED A PLACE ON THE GUARDIAN COUNCIL.

...BUT DON'T ASK ME IF I'M READY.

BECAUSE NO MATTER WHAT HAPPENS, I'LL HAVE TO BE.

END OF BOOK FOUR

for Julie

CREATED AT

BOLT CITY

P R O D U C T I O N S

IN ALHAMBRA, CALIFORNIA

WRITTEN AND ILLUSTRATED BY
KAZU KIBUISHI

LEAD PRODUCTION ARTIST
JASON CAFFOE

COLORS & BACKGROUND
JASON CAFFOE
ZANE YARBROUGH
KAZU KIBUISHI

PAGE FLATTING

DENVER JACKSON
JON LEE
STUART LIVINGSTON
RIKKI SIMONS
MICHAEL REGINA
KEAN SOO

SPECIAL THANKS

GORDON LUK, AMY KIM KIBUISHI, JUDY HANSEN,
DAVID SAYLOR, PHIL FALCO, CASSANDRA PELHAM,
BEN ZHU & THE GALLERY NUCLEUS CREW, NICK
& MELISSA HARRIS, NANCY CAFFOE, OVERBROOK
ENTERTAINMENT, THE FLIGHT ARTISTS, TAKA
KIBUISHI, TIM GANTER, RACHEL ORMISTON,
KHANG LE & ADHESIVE GAMES, OVI NEDELCU,
TAO AKASHI, JUNE KIBUISHI, SUNNI KIM, ARDEN
KÖPRÜLÜYAN & TUDEM PUBLISHING, SHEILA
MARIE EVERETT, ANTHONY WU, ERIC WU, JEFF
SMITH, STEVE HAMAKER, JENNY ROBB, SCOTT
MCCLOUD, & JUNI.

ABOUT THE AUTHOR

Kazu Kibuishi is the creator of the #1 *New York Times* bestselling Amulet series. *Amulet, Book One: The Stonekeeper* was an ALA Best Book for Young Adults and a Children's Choice Book Award finalist. He is also the creator of *Copper*, a collection of his popular webcomic that features an adventuresome boy-and-dog pair. Kazu also illustrated the covers of the 15th anniversary paperback editions of the Harry Potter series written by J. K. Rowling. He lives and works in Seattle, Washington, with his wife, Amy Kim Kibuishi, and their children.

Visit Kazu online at www.boltcity.com.

MAP
OF CIELIS

1. Zeppelin Keep
2. Garden of Keepers
3. Guardian Castle
4. Council Chamber
5. Yarboro Prison
6. Shipbuilder's Market
7. Airship Docks
8. Nimbus Square
9. Cielan Span
10. Waterfall Corridor

CATACOMBS
OF CIELIS

1. MOTHER STONE CHAMBER
2. STONECUTTER ALCOVE
3. GUARDIAN TOMB
4. STRATUS CISTERN
5. HEXAGON FIELD
6. STONEKEEPER CATHEDRAL
7. COLOSSAL HALLS

8. TRANSPORE
9. ALTO CISTERN
10. NIMBUS CISTERN
11. ROBOT MINES
12. COLOSSUS WORKSHOP
13. TRANSPORE
14. CRYSTAL GROTTO

ALSO BY KAZU KIBUISHI

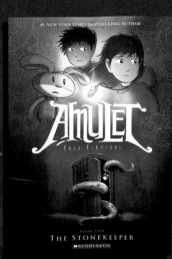

BOOK ONE
THE STONEKEEPER

BOOK TWO
THE STONEKEEPER'S CURSE

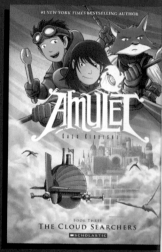

BOOK THREE
THE CLOUD SEARCHERS

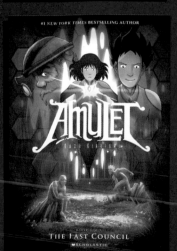

BOOK FOUR
THE LAST COUNCIL

BOOK FIVE
PRINCE OF THE ELVES

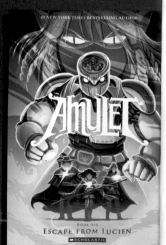

BOOK SIX
ESCAPE FROM LUCIEN